FOOD
JOURNAL

Bonnie Marcus Collection

When you feel good, it shows...

The Bonnie Marcus Food Journal is more than a notebook to keep a record of your food and exercise: it's a place to write, read, doodle and feel inspired – your indispensable guide to the diet dilemmas of a modern girl. We've made sure that it's packed full of little snippets to amuse, advise or motivate, plus recipes to help to confirm your status as a domestic goddess.

This journey isn't just about losing weight: it's about finding yourself. We want to help you make the most of every day and be mindful about what you put into your body (it is a temple, after all). With a little savvy advice, you can navigate 21st-century womanhood, in heels!

The secret of getting ahead is getting started!

Dieting doesn't have to wait until Monday – don't put it off any longer. Pick a date and stick to it!

What did you eat today?

DATE

06 . 09 . 19

● Breakfast

Nutella on bread with milk and a drinkable yoghurt.

● Lunch

Chicken sandwitch with cucumbers and raisins.

● Dinner

Frankfurt's with a wrap and cucumbers.

16.16g 6.8g

● Snacks

apple , banana , kellogs bar (rice krispies), two raisan packets and two glasses of water.

83
? 2.2g   1.7g 83 kcal
47 0.1g ✗ 47 11.2g
✗   ✗   ✗   ✗
16.16g

TOTAL

5

Wholemeal muffins

200 g/7 oz wholemeal flour
2 tsp baking powder
2 tbsp light muscovado sugar
100 g/3½ oz ready-to-use dried apricots,
  finely chopped
1 banana, mashed with 1 tbsp orange juice
1 tsp finely grated orange rind

300 ml/10 fl oz skimmed milk
1 egg, beaten
3 tbsp rapeseed oil or sunflower oil
2 tbsp porridge oats
honey or maple syrup, to serve

1. Preheat the oven to 200°C/400°F/Gas Mark 6. Place 10 paper muffin cases in a 12-hole deep bun tin. Sift the flour and baking powder into a mixing bowl, adding any husks that remain in the sieve. Stir in the sugar and chopped apricots.

2. Make a well in the centre of the dry ingredients and add the banana, orange rind, milk, beaten egg and oil. Mix together well to form a thick batter. Divide the batter evenly between the 10 paper cases.

3. Sprinkle each muffin with a few porridge oats and bake in the preheated oven for 25–30 minutes, or until well risen and firm to the touch. Transfer the muffins to a wire rack to cool slightly. Serve the muffins warm with a little honey or maple syrup.

What did you eat today?

DATE

....

● **Breakfast**

....

....

● **Lunch**

....

....

● **Dinner**

....

....

● **Snacks**

....

....

....

....

	Calories	Fat	Sat Fat	Carbs
Breakfast				
Lunch				
Dinner				
Snacks				
TOTAL				

● **NOTES**

What did you eat today?

DATE

. . . .

	Calories	Fat	Sat Fat	Carbs

- **Breakfast**

. . . .

. . . .

- **Lunch**

. . . .

. . . .

- **Dinner**

. . . .

. . . .

- **Snacks**

. . . .

. . . .

. . . .

. . . .

TOTAL

- **NOTES**

9

The people who will love you at your worst...

Add pictures of the ones who love you best!

What did you eat today?

DATE
....

	Calories	Fat	Sat Fat	Carbs

● **Breakfast**
....
....

● **Lunch**
....
....

● **Dinner**
....
....

● **Snacks**
....
....
....
....

TOTAL

☼ **NOTES**

What did you eat today?

DATE
....

	Calories	Fat	Sat Fat	Carbs

● **Breakfast**
....
....

● **Lunch**
....
....

● **Dinner**
....
....

● **Snacks**
....
....
....
....

TOTAL ☐ ☐ ☐ ☐

⚙ **NOTES**

Diet-friendly brownie bites

● **MAKES 36**

175 g/6 oz dark chocolate,
  broken into small pieces
2 eggs
1 tsp vanilla extract
150 g/5½ oz soft dark brown sugar
150 ml/5 fl oz sunflower oil, plus extra
  for greasing

4 cooked beetroot, grated
100 g/3½ oz plain flour
¾ tsp baking powder
3 tbsp cocoa powder

1. Preheat the oven to 180°C/350°F/Gas Mark 4. Lightly grease a 20-cm/8-inch square baking tin and line with baking paper.

2. Put the chocolate in a heatproof bowl set over a saucepan of gently simmering water and heat until just melted. Remove from the heat.

3. Put the eggs, vanilla and sugar in a bowl and beat at high speed with an electric whisk for 3–4 minutes, or until pale and creamy. Beat in the oil. Stir in the beetroot, then sift in the flour, baking powder and cocoa and fold in. Add the melted chocolate and stir until evenly combined.

4. Spoon the mixture into the prepared tin and bake in the preheated oven for 25–30 minutes, or until just firm to the touch. Leave to cool in the tin, then turn out and cool completely on a wire rack. Cut into 36 bite-sized squares and serve.

● **TIP:** Store the cut brownies in an airtight container – they're best eaten within 1–2 days. Uncut and wrapped in clingfilm, they'll keep at room temperature for up to 4 days, or in the freezer for up to 3 months.

What did you eat today?

	Calories	Fat	Sat Fat	Carbs

DATE ....

 Breakfast
....
....

● **Lunch**
....
....

● **Dinner**
....
....

● **Snacks**
....
....
....
....

TOTAL ☐ ☐ ☐ ☐

✺ NOTES

Be so happy that when others look at you, they feel happy too!

✿ MAKE A LIST OF ALL THE THINGS THAT MAKE YOU SMILE – EVERY LITTLE TRIUMPH IS WORTH CELEBRATING!

What did you eat today?

DATE

....

● **Breakfast**

....

....

● **Lunch**

....

....

● **Dinner**

....

....

● **Snacks**

....

....

....

....

	Calories	Fat	Sat Fat	Carbs
TOTAL				

NOTES

What did you eat today?

	Calories	Fat	Sat Fat	Carbs
DATE				
● **Breakfast**				
....				
....				
● **Lunch**				
....				
....				
● **Dinner**				
....				
....				
● **Snacks**				
....				
....				
....				
....				
TOTAL				

NOTES

21

What did you eat today?

DATE

....

● **Breakfast**

....

....

● **Lunch**

....

....

● **Dinner**

....

....

● **Snacks**

....

....

....

....

	Calories	Fat	Sat Fat	Carbs
TOTAL				

✿ **NOTES**

What did you eat today?

DATE

....

⬤ **Breakfast**

....

....

⬤ **Lunch**

....

....

⬤ **Dinner**

....

....

⬤ **Snacks**

....

....

....

....

	Calories	Fat	Sat Fat	Carbs
TOTAL				

⬤ **NOTES**

23

10 everyday superfoods

Your body is a temple, right? Well superfoods are packed with important nutritional elements for optimum mental and physical health. These 10 ingredients are all things that you'll find in the local grocer's, and they won't break the bank either...

● **APPLES** are your champion fruit if you're on a diet – an average-sized apple contains just 60 calories, and they're low on the glycaemic index (GI) so they keep you fuller for longer. Apples are also an excellent source of potassium, which helps to prevent fluid retention and bloating. They say 'an apple a day keeps the doctor away' and it's true – regular apple-eaters are proven to have smaller waistlines than those who don't!

● **ORANGES** are a great source of vitamin C, which is a natural cold remedy – it helps to fight off infections and reduce the length of coughs and sniffles. Choose the fruit instead of a glass of orange juice (which may have added sweeteners) as the average-sized orange comes in at just 65 calories.

● **BLUEBERRIES** are the original superfood and are a tasty fruit that can easily be added to everyday eating (bake into muffins, sprinkle over porridge or eat as a snack). Regular consumption of blueberries could help to lower your cholesterol, a key influencer of heart health. And, even better, they're said to be a natural fix for pesky bouts of cystitis.

● **BANANAS** have all the necessary nutrients to make them the ultimate sports snack – complex carbs, potassium and fibre mean they are a quality fuel for the body, so grab one after a workout to replenish your body. Although quite high in natural sugars, the average-sized banana is only around 105 calories – an excellent healthy snack.

● **BROCCOLI** is the stuff of most kids' nightmares, but actually it's a really low-calorie vegetable (only 34 calories per 100 g/3½ oz) that's packed with beneficial nutrients like calcium for healthy bones and teeth. Look out for darker-green broccoli – the darker it is, in fact, the better it is for you!

● **CARROTS** contain carotene, which helps to protect against high cholesterol and its associated risk of heart disease, and it's proven that women who eat at least five carrots per week are two thirds less likely to have a stroke than those who consume none. Be careful, though – a very high intake of carrots can cause the skin to take on an orange appearance!

● **TOMATOES** are an excellent addition to salads, as they are extremely low in calories (18 calories per 100 g/3½ oz) and just one medium-sized tomato contains a good portion of vitamin C. Pick tomatoes that are deep red and ripe, as these contain more lycopene, which helps to prevent blood clots.

● **GARLIC** is renowned for its strong flavour – and lingering smell – but if you can get past the inevitable garlic breath, it's a really beneficial addition to your diet. Regular consumption (even in small quantities) can reduce the risk of heart disease.

● **PUMPKIN** contains fat-soluble carotenoids, which help to protect the skin, heart, eyes, brain and liver (all fatty parts of the body). It also contains malic acid, which is important for cell regeneration. Pumpkin's high water content (which is common to all marrows and squashes) means it's very low in calories: 100 g/3½ oz of peeled, chopped pumpkin is just 13 calories.

● **RED PEPPERS** can contain up to two times the amount of vitamin C and nine times the amount of carotene in green peppers. They are a good source of vitamin A, which is used to repair skin damaged by UV light. An average-sized red pepper contains 37 calories, so is a low-calorie ingredient that can be added to all sorts of family-friendly dishes (chilli, pasta sauce, savoury bakes and stews).

What did you eat today?

DATE

....

● **Breakfast**

....

....

● **Lunch**

....

....

● **Dinner**

....

....

● **Snacks**

....

....

....

....

	Calories	Fat	Sat Fat	Carbs
TOTAL				

● **NOTES**

What did you eat today?

DATE

	Calories	Fat	Sat Fat	Carbs

● **Breakfast**

● **Lunch**

● **Dinner**

● **Snacks**

TOTAL

● **NOTES**

Mojito ice pops

● **MAKES 8**

juice of 6 limes
600 ml/1 pint chilled soda water
leaves from 1 bunch of fresh mint
3 limes, cut into wedges
100 g/3½ oz caster sugar
2 tbsp white rum

1. Put the lime juice and soda water into a large jug and stir together well.

2. Stir in the mint leaves, lime wedges, sugar and rum. Using a muddler, wooden spoon or mallet, mash together all the ingredients until well blended.

3. Pour the mixture into eight 100-ml/3½-fl oz ice pop moulds. Divide the lime wedges and mint leaves evenly between them. Insert the ice pop sticks and freeze for 10–12 hours, or until firm. If you are using shop-bought moulds with their own plastic sticks, follow the manufacturer's directions for inserting the sticks. If your moulds don't come with sticks, use wooden ones. To hold the sticks in place while your ice pop freezes, cover the filled moulds with foil and make a small slit with a sharp knife in the centre. Insert the stick and it will be secure until your ice pop is frozen.

4. To unmould the ice pops, dip the frozen moulds into warm water for a few seconds and gently release the pops while holding the sticks. Eat within 3 months of freezing.

● **TIP:** Once they're unmoulded, ice pops can be eaten right away, but it's best to wait a bit. Wrap pops in plastic food bags or clingfilm and freeze for at least 30 minutes. This second freezing means the ice pops won't melt as quickly while you're eating them.

No matter how slow you go, you are still lapping everybody on the sofa.

Studies have shown that many of us put on weight not because we are eating more than we used to, but because we burn fewer calories through activity. Cars, home appliances, the Internet, TV, office jobs, escalators and lifts all help to keep us sedentary. Exercise not only helps you to keep your weight stable (and can help you to lose any extra pounds) but also improves sleep patterns, helps lift depression, improves posture, increases strength and mobility, and improves heart and lung health.

The best exercise is anything you can do without huge expense, or adjusting your lifestyle too much. Walking is ideal – you can do it anywhere, any time and it's free. Try taking the stairs not the lift, or walking one extra stop instead of taking the bus all the way. Try to do at least 30 minutes a day, five days a week.

You don't have to feel the burn to see the benefit. Burn off some extra calories while cleaning around the house...

Vacuuming – 180 Cals*
Dusting – 170 Cals*
Gardening – 250 Cals*
Mopping floors – 190 Cals*
Washing windows – 180 Cals*
Ironing – 110 Cals*

*Values given are approximate number of calories burnt in 1 hour. Calories burnt depend on height, weight and vigour of movement, and will differ from person to person.

What did you eat today?

DATE

....

	Calories	Fat	Sat Fat	Carbs

- **Breakfast**

....

....

- **Lunch**

....

....

- **Dinner**

....

....

- **Snacks**

....

....

....

....

TOTAL

NOTES

✿ TODAY I WISH...

....
....
....
....
....
....
....
....

Turn I wish into I will...

What did you eat today?

DATE

....

● **Breakfast**

....

....

● **Lunch**

....

....

● **Dinner**

....

....

● **Snacks**

....

....

....

....

TOTAL

Calories	Fat	Sat Fat	Carbs

● **NOTES**

What did you eat today?

DATE
....

	Calories	Fat	Sat Fat	Carbs

● **Breakfast**
....
....

● **Lunch**
....
....

● **Dinner**
....
....

● **Snacks**
....
....
....
....

TOTAL

NOTES

What did you eat today?

DATE

....

	Calories	Fat	Sat Fat	Carbs

● **Breakfast**

....

....

● **Lunch**

....

....

● **Dinner**

....

....

● **Snacks**

....

....

....

....

TOTAL

☀ NOTES

What did you eat today?

	Calories	Fat	Sat Fat	Carbs

DATE
....

⬤ **Breakfast**
....
....

⬤ **Lunch**
....
....

⬤ **Dinner**
....
....

⬤ **Snacks**
....
....
....
....

TOTAL

✿ **NOTES**

Red salad with beetroot & radish

● SERVES 4

8 small cooked beetroot, quartered
1 small red onion, cut into thin wedges
1 bunch radishes, sliced
1 tbsp chopped fresh mint
100 ml/3½ fl oz extra virgin olive oil
1 tbsp wholegrain mustard

1 tbsp balsamic vinegar
1 tbsp lemon juice
2 tsp honey
salt and pepper
flatbread, to serve

1. Toss together the beetroot, onion and radishes and stir in half the mint. Arrange on four serving plates.

2. To make the dressing, put the oil, mustard, vinegar, lemon juice and honey into a screw-top jar and shake well to mix. Season with salt and pepper to taste.

3. Spoon the dressing over the salad and sprinkle the remaining mint on top. Serve immediately, with flatbread.

Avocado, feta & rocket salad

● **SERVES 4**

2 ripe avocados
4 handfuls rocket
125 g/4½ oz feta cheese, crumbled
100 ml/3½ fl oz olive oil
2 tbsp white wine vinegar
1 shallot, finely chopped

1 large ripe tomato, deseeded and diced
1 tbsp lemon juice
1 tsp granulated sugar
salt and pepper

1. Halve, peel, stone and slice the avocados and arrange on a serving dish with the rocket. Top with the feta cheese.

2. To make the dressing, put the oil and vinegar into a saucepan and gently heat, then add the shallot and cook, stirring for 2–3 minutes until soft. Add the tomato, lemon juice and sugar and gently heat, stirring, for 30 seconds.

3. Season the dressing with salt and pepper, then spoon it over the salad and serve immediately.

What did you eat today?

DATE

....

● **Breakfast**

....

....

● **Lunch**

....

....

● **Dinner**

....

....

● **Snacks**

....

....

....

....

	Calories	Fat	Sat Fat	Carbs
TOTAL				

● **NOTES**

What did you eat today?

	Calories	Fat	Sat Fat	Carbs

DATE

....

● **Breakfast**

....

....

● **Lunch**

....

....

● **Dinner**

....

....

● **Snacks**

....

....

....

....

TOTAL

NOTES

What did you eat today?

DATE

....

● **Breakfast**

....

....

● **Lunch**

....

....

● **Dinner**

....

....

● **Snacks**

....

....

....

....

TOTAL

Calories	Fat	Sat Fat	Carbs

● **NOTES**

What did you eat today?

	Calories	Fat	Sat Fat	Carbs
DATE				
Breakfast				
Lunch				
Dinner				
Snacks				
TOTAL				

✿ NOTES

My favourite new recipes...

● **RECIPE** ....

Source ....

Ingredients ....

....

....

....

....

Method ....

....

....

....

....

....

....

....

....

....

What did you eat today?

DATE

....

● **Breakfast**

....

....

● **Lunch**

....

....

● **Dinner**

....

....

● **Snacks**

....

....

....

....

	Calories	Fat	Sat Fat	Carbs
TOTAL				

⚙ **NOTES**

Never underestimate the restorative powers of a hot bath. Always make time to soak your troubles away.

"Cheers! Here's to a glass of bubbles that comes in at under 100 calories per glass."

Strawberry fizz

● **SERVES 4**

225 g/8 oz fresh strawberries, hulled
2 tbsp agave syrup
juice of 1 lime
8 tbsp crushed ice
100 ml/3½ oz vodka
400 ml/14 fl oz diet cola
whole strawberries and strips of lime zest, to decorate

1. Put the strawberries, syrup and lime in a large jug and process with an electric stick blender or in a food processor until smooth.

2. Add 2 tablespoons of crushed ice to each of four glasses.

3. Pour the strawberry mixture evenly into each glass, add 2 tablespoons of vodka to each glass and stir to mix.

4. Top up the glasses with the cola to taste, place whole strawberries and strips of lime zest on the rims, and serve immediately.

● **TIP:** To add an extra-fabulous finish to your low-cal cocktail, make a tray of decorative ice cubes. Half-fill ice-cube trays with water and freeze until firm. Dip edible flowers into cold water, then place in the ice-cube trays. Top up with water and freeze.

What did you eat today?

DATE

	Calories	Fat	Sat Fat	Carbs

Breakfast

....

....

Lunch

....

....

Dinner

....

....

Snacks

....

....

....

....

TOTAL

NOTES

What did you eat today?

	Calories	Fat	Sat Fat	Carbs

DATE

....

● **Breakfast**

....

....

● **Lunch**

....

....

● **Dinner**

....

....

● **Snacks**

....

....

....

....

TOTAL

● **NOTES**

What did you eat today?

DATE

	Calories	Fat	Sat Fat	Carbs

● **Breakfast**

● **Lunch**

● **Dinner**

● **Snacks**

TOTAL

● **NOTES**

What did you eat today?

DATE

	Calories	Fat	Sat Fat	Carbs

● **Breakfast**

● **Lunch**

● **Dinner**

● **Snacks**

TOTAL

● **NOTES**

200-calorie chocolate soufflés

● MAKES 6

vegetable oil spray
25 g/1 oz unsalted butter
75 g/3 oz dark chocolate,
  finely chopped
175 ml/6 fl oz skimmed milk
4 tbsp cocoa powder

1 tbsp all-purpose flour
1 tsp vanilla extract
pinch of salt
4 egg whites
100 g/3½ oz granulated sugar

1. Preheat the oven to 190°C/375°F/Gas Mark 5. Spray six 175-ml/6-fl oz ramekins with vegetable oil spray. Put the butter, chocolate and 4 tablespoons of the milk in a small bowl and microwave on high for 30 seconds. Stir until the chocolate is melted. Add the cocoa powder, flour, vanilla extract and salt, and beat until well mixed. Add the remaining milk and stir to combine.

2. In a large bowl, beat the egg whites with an electric whisk on high speed for about 3 minutes, or until stiff peaks form. Add the sugar, a little at a time, and continue to beat for about another 2 minutes, or until the mixture is thick and glossy.

3. Gently fold a large dollop of the egg mixture into the chocolate mixture and stir to combine using a rubber palette knife. Gently fold the chocolate mixture into the remaining egg whites until well combined.

4. Carefully spoon the mixture into the prepared ramekins and bake in the preheated oven for about 22–25 minutes, or until the soufflés are puffy and dry on the top. Serve immediately.

You're never too old to splash in the puddles and dance in the rain!

© Bonnie Marcus

What did you eat today?

DATE

	Calories	Fat	Sat Fat	Carbs
Breakfast				
Lunch				
Dinner				
Snacks				
TOTAL				

☼ NOTES

What did you eat today?

DATE ....

	Calories	Fat	Sat Fat	Carbs

● **Breakfast**
....
....

● **Lunch**
....
....

● **Dinner**
....
....

● **Snacks**
....
....
....
....

TOTAL

NOTES

What did you eat today?

DATE ....

	Calories	Fat	Sat Fat	Carbs

● **Breakfast**
....
....

● **Lunch**
....
....

● **Dinner**
....
....

● **Snacks**
....
....
....
....

TOTAL

NOTES

What did you eat today?

	Calories	Fat	Sat Fat	Carbs
DATE				
Breakfast				
Lunch				
Dinner				
Snacks				
TOTAL				

NOTES

What did you eat today?

DATE

....

	Calories	Fat	Sat Fat	Carbs

- **Breakfast**

....
....

- **Lunch**

....
....

- **Dinner**

....
....

- **Snacks**

....
....
....
....

TOTAL

☼ NOTES

A balanced diet

A balanced diet means eating a wide variety of foods in the right proportions. If we can balance the major calorie-providing nutrients such as carbohydrates, fats and protein, then they should provide all of the other elements essential to a healthy diet – vitamins, minerals and plant chemical compounds, as well as dietary fibre.

20 PER CENT

5 PER CENT

12 PER CENT

33 PER CENT

30 PER CENT

● 33 PER CENT Fruit and vegetables

These are the richest providers of many vitamins, plant chemicals and fibre. At least five portions every day are preferable and the ideal balance is two fruits and three vegetables. Choose a rainbow of different colours to ensure you get a complete range of nutrients.

● 30 PER CENT Starchy foods

Starchy foods such as grains (preferably whole), bread, pasta and root vegetables provide a range of vitamins, minerals, plant chemicals and fibre, as well as the calories we need.

● 20 PER CENT Lean meat, eggs, fish, shellfish, nuts and seeds

Vary your choices within this section; it's good to eat fish regularly (including oily fish), but also have meals that include pulses, such as beans or lentils, or nuts and seeds.

● 12 PER CENT Dairy or soya protein

Including milk, cheese and yogurt, or calcium-fortified soya milk and yogurts. Cream and cream cheeses aren't included because they contain little protein and lots of saturated fat.

● 5 PER CENT High-fat or high-sugar foods

These are what might be called 'junk foods' and should be eaten in small amounts (or not at all, if possible). This includes sugar, sugary drinks, cake, biscuits, pastries and sweets.

Pumpkin & haricot bean slimmers' soup

● **SERVES 4**

1 tsp olive oil
1 red onion, chopped
2 garlic cloves, crushed
450 g/1 lb pumpkin or other winter
   squash, peeled, seeded and chopped
   (prepared wieght)
2 tsp smoked paprika

¾ tsp chilli flakes
5–6 fresh sage leaves, finely chopped
900 ml/1½ pints vegetable stock
1 x 400-ml can haricot beans, drained
salt and pepper, to taste
crème fraîche and chopped spring onions,
   to serve

1. Heat the oil in a large heavy-based saucepan and sauté the onion and garlic for 3–4 minutes. Add the pumpkin and cook for a further 4–5 minutes.

2. Add the paprika, chilli flakes and sage and cook for 1 minute, stirring all the time.

3. Add the stock, season with salt and pepper, cover and simmer for 20–25 minutes, or until the pumpkin is tender. Leave the soup to cool slightly, then process using an electric stick blender, until smooth.

4. Stir in the haricot beans and heat through for 2–3 minutes. Serve with a spoonful of crème fraîche and a sprinkle of chopped spring onions.

● **TIP:** One serving of this super healthy soup is just 130 calories. A portion also contains just 1.5 g of fat, of which only 0.5 g is saturated fat.

What did you eat today?

DATE

....

● **Breakfast**

....

....

● **Lunch**

....

....

● **Dinner**

....

....

● **Snacks**

....

....

....

....

	Calories	Fat	Sat Fat	Carbs
TOTAL				

NOTES

Dorothy is proof that with a
fabulous pair of heels you can
do anything!

Life is sweet!

IT'S OK TO INDULGE ONCE IN A WHILE...

What did you eat today?

DATE

....

● **Breakfast**

....

....

● **Lunch**

....

....

● **Dinner**

....

....

● **Snacks**

....

....

....

....

	Calories	Fat	Sat Fat	Carbs
Breakfast				
Lunch				
Dinner				
Snacks				
TOTAL				

☼ **NOTES**

Peachy wake-up call

1 medium sweet potato, cut in
  half lengthways
1-cm/½-inch piece fresh ginger
3 carrots, scrubbed
3 peaches, halved and stoned
pinch ground mixed spice (optional)

Feed all the ingredients through
a juicer – the sweet potato is quite
hard so make sure that the juicer is
on high speed. Pour the juice into a glass
half-filled with ice and sprinkle with
a little ground mixed spice (if using).

Power-boosting beetroot

● **MAKES 1**

2 raw beetroot, leaves trimmed off
2 large carrots
2 celery sticks, halved
5-cm/2-inch piece cucumber
2 red-skinned dessert apples, halved
2 tbsp ground walnuts

Feed all the vegetables and apples through
a juicer. Stir the finely ground walnuts
into the juice then pour into a glass
half-filled with ice and serve.

Spiced berry bombshell

● **MAKES 1**

3 large ripe red-skinned plums,
   halved and stoned
handful of red or green curly kale
1 ripe pear, cored and halved
150 g/5½ oz blackberries
2 tbsp wheat-germ powder
pinch ground cinnamon

Add the plums and kale to a juicer chute,
then add the pear and extract the juice.
Pour the juice into a blender, add the
blackberries, wheat germ, a little ground
cinnamon and a handful of ice. Blitz until
smooth. Add water, if needed. Pour into a
glass and serve.

Strawberry supercharge

● **MAKES 1**

300 g/10 oz strawberries, hulled
½ large pomegranate, seeds popped out
   from the casing
2 apples, halved
crushed ice (optional)

Feed the strawberries, pomegranate
seeds and apples through a juicer – to
maximize the juice make sure that the
juicer is on low speed. Stir well, then
pour into a glass and drink as soon as
you can on its own or with some crushed
ice (if using).

✿ LIST YOUR LONG-TERM HEALTH GOALS, AND HOW YOU AIM TO GET THERE…

Every masterpiece starts with a blank canvas!

What did you eat today?

DATE

....

● **Breakfast**

....

....

● **Lunch**

....

....

● **Dinner**

....

....

● **Snacks**

....

....

....

....

TOTAL

Calories	Fat	Sar Fat	Carbs

◎ NOTES

What did you eat today?

DATE

....

● **Breakfast**

....

....

● **Lunch**

....

....

● **Dinner**

....

....

● **Snacks**

....

....

....

....

	Calories	Fat	Sat Fat	Carbs
TOTAL				

⚙ NOTES

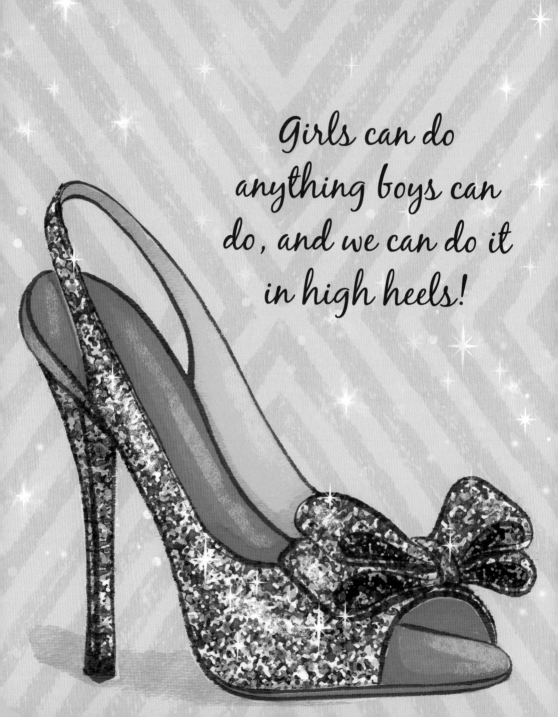

Girls can do
anything boys can
do, and we can do it
in high heels!

What did you eat today?

	Calories	Fat	Sat Fat	Carbs

DATE ....

● **Breakfast**
....
....

● **Lunch**
....
....

● **Dinner**
....
....

● **Snacks**
....
....
....

TOTAL

✿ NOTES

Angel food cake

● **SERVES 10**

sunflower oil, for greasing
8 large egg whites
1 tsp cream of tartar
1 tsp almond extract
250 g/9 oz caster sugar
125 g/4½ oz plain flour, plus extra
  for dusting

To decorate
250 g/9 oz mixed berries, such as
  raspberries, redcurrants and blueberries
1 tbsp lemon juice
2 tbsp icing sugar

1. Preheat the oven to 160°C/325°F/Gas Mark 3. Grease and lightly flour a 23-cm/9-inch ring mould.

2. In a clean grease-free bowl, beat the egg whites until they hold soft peaks. Add the cream of tartar and beat again until the whites are stiff but not dry. Beat in the almond extract, then add the caster sugar, a tablespoon at a time, beating hard between each addition. Sift in the flour and fold in lightly and evenly, using a large metal spoon.

3. Spoon the mixture into the prepared cake mould. Bake in the preheated oven for 40–45 minutes, or until golden brown. Run the tip of a knife around the edges of the cake to loosen from the mould. Leave to cool in the mould for 10 minutes, then turn out onto a wire rack to cool.

4. To decorate, place the berries, lemon juice and icing sugar in a saucepan and heat until the sugar has dissolved. Spoon over the top of the cake.

"At just 170 calories per serving, this cake is as virtuous as it sounds. Plus, with only 0.5 g of fat per slice, you can afford to add a layer of air-light vanilla icing, if you're feeling naughty!"

COFFEE
MORNING
CLASSIC

☀ WRITE DOWN FIVE THINGS THAT MADE YOU HAPPY TODAY…

1. ....
....
....

2. ....
....
....

3. ....
....
....

4. ....
....
....

5. ....
....
....

I have chosen to be happy because it is good for my health!

What did you eat today?

DATE

....

● **Breakfast**

....

....

● **Lunch**

....

....

● **Dinner**

....

....

● **Snacks**

....

....

....

....

TOTAL

Calories	Fat	Sat Fat	Carbs

☼ NOTES

The most memorable days usually end with the dirtiest clothes…

What did you eat today?

DATE

....

● **Breakfast**

....

....

● **Lunch**

....

....

● **Dinner**

....

....

● **Snacks**

....

....

....

....

	Calories	Fat	Sat Fat	Carbs
TOTAL				

☼ NOTES

What did you eat today?

DATE

. . . .

		Calories	Fat	Sat Fat	Carbs

● **Breakfast**

. . . .

. . . .

● **Lunch**

. . . .

. . . .

● **Dinner**

. . . .

. . . .

● **Snacks**

. . . .

. . . .

. . . .

TOTAL

● **NOTES**

What did you eat today?

DATE ....

	Calories	Fat	Sat Fat	Carbs

● **Breakfast**

....

....

● **Lunch**

....

....

● **Dinner**

....

....

● **Snacks**

....

....

....

....

TOTAL

● **NOTES**

What did you eat today?

DATE

	Calories	Fat	Sat Fat	Carbs
Breakfast				
Lunch				
Dinner				
Snacks				
TOTAL				

NOTES

What did you eat today?

DATE ....

	Calories	Fat	Sat Fat	Carbs

● **Breakfast**
....

....

● **Lunch**
....

....

● **Dinner**
....

....

● **Snacks**
....

....

....

....

TOTAL

● **NOTES**

88

What did you eat today?

DATE
....

	Calories	Fat	Sat Fat	Carbs

● **Breakfast**
....
....

● **Lunch**
....
....

● **Dinner**
....
....

● **Snacks**
....
....
....
....

TOTAL

● **NOTES**

89

What did you eat today?

DATE

....

● **Breakfast**

....

....

● **Lunch**

....

....

● **Dinner**

....

....

● **Snacks**

....

....

....

....

TOTAL

Calories	Fat	Sat Fat	Carbs

✿ NOTES

90

What did you eat today?

DATE
....

	Calories	Fat	Sat Fat	Carbs

● **Breakfast**
....
....

● **Lunch**
....
....

● **Dinner**
....
....

● **Snacks**
....
....
....
....

TOTAL

● **NOTES**

What did you eat today?

DATE

....

● **Breakfast**

....

....

● **Lunch**

....

....

● **Dinner**

....

....

● **Snacks**

....

....

....

....

	Calories	Fat	Sat Fat	Carbs
TOTAL				

NOTES

What did you eat today?

DATE

....

	Calories	Fat	Sat Fat	Carbs

● **Breakfast**

....

....

● **Lunch**

....

....

● **Dinner**

....

....

● **Snacks**

....

....

....

....

TOTAL

Calories	Fat	Sat Fat	Carbs

NOTES

You don't have to
be great to start,
but you have to start
to be great.

Hobbies might seem like a luxury reserved for those who lead a quiet life, but conversely they can be an incredibly important part of a busy lifestyle. A good hobby can provide a slice of work-free time in your schedule, and is a great opportunity to recharge your batteries by doing something you enjoy. It's a great excuse to make a regular fixture with the girls, so use the social aspect of hobbies as another excuse to get motivated. Aerobic activity (no matter how strenuous) encourages regular sleeping patterns, so making time in a full schedule for a workout could actually help you to feel well rested and re-energized.

❀ MAKE A LIST OF NEW HOBBIES YOU COULD ADD TO YOUR WEEKLY SCHEDULE...

My favourite new recipes...

● **RECIPE** ....

Source ....

Ingredients ....

....

....

....

....

Method ....

....

....

....

....

....

....

....

....

My favourite new recipes...

● **RECIPE** ....

Source ....

Ingredients ....

....

....

....

....

Method ....

....

....

....

....

....

....

....

....

....

....

What did you eat today?

DATE
....

● **Breakfast**
....
....

● **Lunch**
....
....

● **Dinner**
....
....

● **Snacks**
....
....
....
....

	Calories	Fat	Sat Fat	Carbs
TOTAL				

✿ NOTES

These mini sweet bites are virtuous because of their size – but at fewer than 150 calories per baby brûlée, you can afford to treat yourself without feeling guilty!

150-calorie baby brûlées

● **MAKES 12**

150 g/5½ oz blueberries
4 egg yolks
1 tsp vanilla extract
100 g/3½ oz caster or granulated sugar
300 ml/10 fl oz double cream

1. Preheat the oven to 160°C/325°F/Gas Mark 3. Put twelve 60-ml/2-fl oz ovenproof dishes in a large roasting pan and divide the blueberries between them.

2. Put the egg yolks, vanilla and 3 tablespoons of the sugar into a small bowl and mix together, using a fork, until smooth and creamy. Pour the cream into a small heavy saucepan, bring to the boil, then gradually mix it into the yolks. Pour the mixture through a sieve into the pan before pouring it back into the bowl.

3. Pour the cream mixture over the blueberries. Pour warm water into the roasting tin to come halfway up the sides of the dishes. Bake in the preheated oven for 15 minutes, or until the custard is just set, with a slight wobble in the centre.

4. Leave to cool for 5–10 minutes, then lift the dishes out of the water and transfer to the fridge to chill for 3–4 hours.

5. To serve, sprinkle the remaining sugar over the dishes in an even layer, then caramelize it using a cook's blowtorch or under a grill preheated to hot.

Keep your head
high, and your
heels higher!

What did you eat today?

DATE

....

● **Breakfast**

....

....

● **Lunch**

....

....

● **Dinner**

....

....

● **Snacks**

....

....

....

....

	Calories	Fat	Sat Fat	Carbs
Breakfast				
Lunch				
Dinner				
Snacks				
TOTAL				

NOTES

Light toffee popcorn

● **MAKES ABOUT 200 G/7 OZ**

70 g/2½ oz unsalted butter
60 g/2¼ oz popping corn
4 tbsp soft dark brown sugar
2 tbsp golden syrup

1. Melt 2 tablespoons of the butter in a large heavy saucepan. Add the popping corn and swirl the pan to coat the corn evenly.

2. Cover the pan with a tight-fitting lid, reduce the heat to low when the corn starts popping. Shake the pan a couple of times to move the unpopped pieces to the bottom. As soon as the popping stops, take the pan off the heat and leave covered.

3. For the toffee coating, melt the remaining butter in a medium heavy saucepan. Add the sugar and syrup and cook over a high heat, stirring, for 1–2 minutes, or until the sugar has dissolved.

4. Pour the toffee coating over the popped corn, replace the lid on the pan and shake well. Leave to cool slightly, then serve immediately.

Skinny hot choc

● **SERVES 1–2**

1 tbsp granulated sugar
2 tbsp cocoa powder
225 ml/8 fl oz skimmed milk
¼ tsp vanilla extract
chocolate curls, to decorate (optional)

1. In a small saucepan, combine the sugar, cocoa powder and about 2 tablespoons of the milk. Stir to make a paste.

2. Add the remaining milk and heat to a simmer over a medium heat. Cook, stirring occasionally, for about 3 minutes until the cocoa and sugar have completely dissolved.

3. Stir in the vanilla extract and serve immediately, topped with chocolate curls (if using).

Vitamins & minerals

Some of the most important nutrients for health are those that we need only in small amounts but are essential for good health. Vitamins and minerals are needed for the day-to-day functioning, protection and maintenance of our bodies...

....

● **VITAMINS that we need regularly but not necessarily every day because they can be stored in the body are:**

Vitamin A – For healthy growth, skin and vision, found mainly in meat, dairy produce and eggs. The body can also convert carotenoids, found in brightly coloured plant foods, into vitamin A.

Vitamin D – For calcium absorption and other functions, found in oily fish and eggs.

Vitamin E – A powerful antioxidant that helps prevent heart disease, found in nuts, seeds, other plant oils and some other plant foods.

Vitamin K – For normal blood clotting, found in a wide variety of foods.

● **VITAMINS we need daily, ideally, because they cannot be stored in the body are:**

Vitamin C – For the immune system, to help iron absorption and many other roles, for example as an antioxidant. Found in fruit and vegetables.

Vitamin B group – These work together for growth, a healthy nervous system and food metabolism. Found in meat, fish, pulses, eggs and dairy produce.

● MINERALS that we often lack enough of are:

Calcium – For healthy bones and with several other roles within the body, found in dairy produce, nuts, seeds and dried fruit.

Iron – For healthy blood and transportation of oxygen, found in meat, pulses, whole grains and leafy greens.

Magnesium – For bone density and a healthy nervous system, heart and muscles, found in nuts, seeds and dairy produce.

Potassium – For regulating blood pressure and for a healthy heart, found in meat, fruit and vegetables.

Zinc – For a healthy immune system, skin and fertility, found in red meat, shellfish, nuts and seeds.

Selenium – For a healthy immune system, found in nuts, pulses and fish.

What did you eat today?

DATE

	Calories	Fat	Sat Fat	Carbs

● **Breakfast**

....

....

● **Lunch**

....

....

● **Dinner**

....

....

● **Snacks**

....

....

....

....

TOTAL

❀ **NOTES**

What did you eat today?

DATE ....

	Calories	Fat	Sat Fat	Carbs

● **Breakfast**
....
....

● **Lunch**
....
....

● **Dinner**
....
....

● **Snacks**
....
....
....
....

TOTAL

● **NOTES**

Veggie burgers

400-ml can red kidney beans,
   drained and rinsed
400-ml can chickpeas,
   drained and rinsed
1 egg yolk
¼ tsp smoked paprika
50 g/1¾ oz fresh breadcrumbs

3 spring onions, finely chopped
vegetable oil, for brushing
4 burger buns, halved
lettuce leaves
tomato slices
4 tbsp soured cream
salt and pepper

1. Preheat the barbecue or grill to high.

2. Put the beans, chickpeas, egg yolk, paprika, breadcrumbs and spring onions in a large bowl and gently mix to combine. Season to taste with salt and pepper. Divide the mixture into four and shape into patties. Season the outside of the patties with salt and pepper and lightly brush with oil.

3. Oil the barbecue grate or grill rack. Cook the burgers for 5 minutes on each side, or until cooked through. Brush the inside of the buns with oil and toast for 1–2 minutes. Place some lettuce and tomatoes on each bun base. Add the burgers and top with soured cream and the bun lids. Serve immediately.

What did you eat today?

	Calories	Fat	Sat Fat	Carbs

DATE
....

● **Breakfast**
....
....

● **Lunch**
....
....

● **Dinner**
....
....

● **Snacks**
....
....
....
....

TOTAL

☼ **NOTES**

Be the type of person you want to meet!

White bean & chicken chilli

● **SERVES 6**

1 tbsp vegetable oil
1 onion, diced
2 garlic cloves, finely chopped
1 green pepper, deseeded and diced
1 small jalapeño pepper, deseeded and diced
2 tsp chilli powder
2 tsp dried oregano

1 tsp ground cumin
1 tsp salt
400-ml can white beans, such as cannellini, rinsed and drained
750 ml/1¼ pints chicken stock
450 g/1 lb cooked chicken breasts, shredded
juice of 1 lime
25 g/1 oz fresh coriander, chopped

1. Heat the oil in a large heavy saucepan over a medium–high heat. Add the onion, garlic, green pepper and jalapeño and cook, stirring occasionally, for about 5 minutes, or until soft.

2. Add the chilli powder, oregano, cumin and salt and cook, stirring, for 30 seconds. Add the beans and stock and bring to the boil. Reduce the heat to medium–low and simmer gently, uncovered, for about 20 minutes.

3. Ladle about half of the bean mixture into a blender or food processor and purée. Return the purée to the pan along with the shredded chicken. Simmer for about 10 minutes, or until heated through. Just before serving, stir in the lime juice and fresh coriander. Serve immediately.

Chicken & sun-dried tomato pasta

● **SERVES 6**

115 g/4 oz sun-dried tomatoes
  (not packed in oil)
350 g/12 oz boneless, skinless chicken
  breasts, diced
1 tsp salt
½ tsp pepper

vegetable oil spray
2 garlic cloves
25 g/1 oz fresh basil
1 tbsp olive oil
300 g/10½ oz dried pasta

1. Put the tomatoes in a small bowl and cover with boiling water. Set aside to soak for about 20 minutes until soft, then drain, discarding the soaking liquid.

2. Season the chicken with ½ teaspoon of the salt and the pepper. Coat a large, non-stick frying pan with the vegetable oil spray and heat over a medium–high heat. Add the chicken and cook, stirring occasionally, for about 5 minutes, or until it is cooked through and just beginning to colour. Set aside.

3. Place the rehydrated tomatoes in a food processor along with the garlic and basil and process to a purée. Add the oil and the remaining salt and continue to process until smooth.

4. Cook the pasta according to the packet instructions. Just before draining, scoop out and set aside about 100 ml/3½ oz of the cooking water. Drain the pasta. Toss the hot pasta with the sun-dried tomato purée, chicken and as much of the pasta cooking water as needed to make a sauce that coats the pasta. Serve immediately.

What did you eat today?

DATE

	Calories	Fat	Sat Fat	Carbs

- Breakfast

- Lunch

- Dinner

- Snacks

TOTAL

NOTES

What did you eat today?

DATE ....

	Calories	Fat	Sat Fat	Carbs

● **Breakfast**
....
....

● **Lunch**
....
....

● **Dinner**
....
....

● **Snacks**
....
....
....
....

TOTAL

● **NOTES**

Youth-boosting foods

● WRINKLES

Whatever your age, wrinkles can leave you feeling, well, old! All sorts of lifestyle factors can be linked to wrinkles – smoking, sun damage, squinting, smiling and frowning – all are responsible for the everlasting impressions.

Vitamin C serums are big news in skin care, and promoted as an excellent preventive measure against wrinkles, but they've got a price tag to match such audacious claims! Science says a diet that's high in vitamin C and linoleic acid means you are less prone to wrinkles. Berries are brilliant, too – packed full of antioxidants that are key to protecting skin cells from damage (and preventing damage and disintegration leads to a longer-lasting youthful looks).

Try peaches, strawberries, kiwi fruit and blueberries – they won't turn back time, but they can help to slow the ticking clock!

● DRY SKIN

As your body ages, it produces less oil from the sebaceous glands – this can mean skin that's dry, itchy and prone to eruption (no fun at all). Suddenly all that teenage greasiness doesn't seem so bad.

The best thing you can do to keep your skin looking radiant is drink water – and plenty of it! Creams and serums might provide short-term relief, but good hydration is essential for a good foundation (and it's cheaper!) It's universally accepted that 2 litres/3½ pints of water per day is how much your body needs – but temper this according to your own body, if it feels good then keep at it!

Beyond just water, omega-3 fatty acids are the go-to nutrient that will help soften dry skin and plump it out. Try fish for a high omega-3 content (salmon and tuna are ideal) or linseed, avocado and walnuts are also good. Vitamin A is good for dried-out, flaky skin too – and is easily found in dark, leafy greens like spinach and broccoli.

● SUN DAMAGE

Sun damage has a nasty habit of creeping up on you – and prevention is key to ensuring your skin looks tip-top in years to come. Leathery skin, wrinkles and brown spots are all increasingly harder to reverse the older you get, and beyond the superficial, overexposure can have serious consequences.

Obviously food should never be used to replace a good sunscreen when it comes to limiting sun exposure, but adding a few tomatoes into your daily diet can't hurt. A recent study indicated that lycopene-rich foods, like tomatoes, can improve the skin's ability to protect against UV rays. Adding green tea to your daily routine is also a good defence against the dangers of the sun: the natural anti-inflammatory constituents have been shown to protect against melanoma.

Water watch...
About 2 litres (3½ pints) is the recommended fluid intake per day for an adult female – always carry a bottle of water with you for on-the-go hydration!

Chocolate brownie mix

MAKES 6 X 500-ml/18-fl oz JARS

700 g/1 lb 9 oz plain flour
1½ tsp salt
600 g/1 oz 5 oz muscovado sugar
1.25 kg/2 lb 12 oz granulated sugar

350 g/12 oz cocoa powder
450 g/1 lb toasted, chopped
   hazelnuts (or other nuts)
500 g/1 lb 2 oz mini dark chocolate chips

To prepare the gift jars, add about 115 g/4 oz of the flour to each of six 500-ml/18-fl oz preserving jars. Next, add ¼ teaspoon of salt and 100 g/3½ oz of muscovado sugar. Next add 200 g/7 oz granulated sugar, then about 55 g/2 oz of cocoa powder, 75 g/2½ oz of chopped nuts and 80 g/2¾ oz of chocolate chips. The brownie mix will keep for up to 6 months. Store tightly covered in a cool, dry place.

Attach a tag to each jar with these instructions:
1. Preheat the oven to 180°C/350°F/Gas Mark 4 and grease a 33 x 23-cm/13 x 9-inch baking tin.

2. Transfer the brownie mix from the jar to a large mixing bowl. In a small mixing bowl, beat together 2 large eggs, 2 tablespoons milk and 1 teaspoon vanilla extract. Add the egg mixture to the dry ingredients and mix until well combined. Stir in 115 g/4 oz of melted butter and mix to combine.

3. Transfer the mixture to the prepared tin and bake in the preheated oven for about 20 minutes, until the top is dry and a skewer inserted into the centre comes out mostly clean. Cool completely in the tin on a wire rack. Serve at room temperature.

Blueberry pancake mix

MAKES 6 X 500-ML/18-FL OZ JARS

700 g/1 lb 9 oz plain flour
2 tbsp baking powder
1 tbsp bicarbonate of soda
150 g/5½ oz granulated sugar
1 tbsp ground cinnamon

175 g/6 oz muscovado sugar
200 g/7 oz dried blueberries
85 g/3 oz pecan nuts, chopped

To prepare the gift jars, add about 115 g/4 oz of the flour to each of six 500-ml/18-fl oz preserving jars. Top with 1 teaspoon of baking powder, ½ teaspoon of bicarbonate of soda, 2 tablespoons of granulated sugar, ½ teaspoon of cinnamon, 2 tablespoons of muscovado sugar, 30 g/1 oz of blueberries and 2 tablespoons of pecans. Top each jar with a lid and close it tightly. The pancake mix will keep for up to 6 months. Store tightly covered in a cool, dry place.

Attach a tag to each jar with these instructions:
1. Whisk 225 ml/8 fl oz of buttermilk or milk and 1 egg together in a large bowl. Add the mix from the jar and 25 g/1 oz of melted butter and mix to combine well.

2. Melt a little butter in a frying pan set over a medium–high heat. Ladle the mixture into the hot pan, about 60 ml/2 fl oz at a time. Cook for 2–3 minutes, until bubbles form on the top of the pancake, burst and are not immediately filled in by more mixture. Flip the pancake over and cook for a further 2 minutes or so, until the second side is golden brown. Continue until all of the mixture has been used up. Serve hot, drizzled with maple syrup.

Traditional lemonade

● **SERVES 4**

3 ripe lemons
125 g/4½ oz granulated sugar, or to taste
850 ml/1½ pints boiling water
cracked ice cubes
lemon slices, to decorate

1. Thinly pare the lemon rind.

2. Put the lemon rind into a heatproof bowl with the sugar. Add the boiling water and stir until the sugar has dissolved. Cover and leave to cool.

3. Squeeze the juice from the lemons and pour into the cooled syrup. Strain into a jug. Taste and add more sugar, if needed.

4. Fill four highball glasses with cracked ice cubes, pour in the lemonade and dress with the lemon slices.

"When life gives you lemons, make lemonade!"

Turn can't
into can
and dreams
into plans!

✿ WRITE DOWN FIVE THINGS THAT YOU WANT TO ACHIEVE IN THE FUTURE…

1. ....

2. ....

3. ....

4. ....

5. ....

What did you eat today?

DATE

	Calories	Fat	Sat Fat	Carbs

● **Breakfast**

● **Lunch**

● **Dinner**

● **Snacks**

TOTAL

● **NOTES**

What did you eat today?

DATE

· **Breakfast**

· **Lunch**

· **Dinner**

· **Snacks**

	Calories	Fat	Sat Fat	Carbs
TOTAL				

NOTES

Exfoliating body scrub

Mix together 1 tablespoon of sea salt, 2 tablespoons of olive oil, 1 tablespoon of set honey and 2–3 drops of rose, sweet fennel, or juniper oil in a bowl to make a runny paste. Rub gently onto the skin with a circular motion and rinse off with warm water.

Exfoliating face scrub

Mix 1 tablespoon of honey with 2 tablespoons finely ground almonds and ½ teaspoon lemon juice. Rub gently onto the face and rinse off with warm water.

Antioxidant face masks

DRY SKIN

Take 1 tablespoon of porridge oats and rub well between your fingers. Infuse in 225 ml/8 fl oz of boiling water for 20 minutes. Strain, then mix the oats with 1 tablespoon honey, 1 egg yolk and 1 tablespoon natural yogurt. Apply to the skin with cotton wool and leave on for 15 minutes.

SENSITIVE SKIN

Mix 1 teaspoon aloe vera gel with 1 tablespoon natural yogurt. Apply and leave for 15 minutes.

OILY SKIN

Mix 1 tablespoon dry fuller's earth (available from some make-up supply companies) with 1 egg yolk, ¼ mashed avocado and a little witch hazel to create a smooth mixture, Apply to the skin and leave on for 15 minutes.

MATURE SKIN

Mash a ripe avocado with a little olive oil and apply to the skin. Leave on for 15 minutes.

PAMPER TIME

* Use treatments on the day of making. Avoid contact with eyes. If treatments get into the eyes, rinse well with warm water.

What did you eat today?

DATE

....

- **Breakfast**

....

....

- **Lunch**

....

....

- **Dinner**

....

....

- **Snacks**

....

....

....

....

	Calories	Fat	Sat Fat	Carbs

TOTAL

❂ NOTES

130

What did you eat today?

DATE

....

	Calories	Fat	Sat Fat	Carbs
Breakfast				
....				
....				
Lunch				
....				
....				
Dinner				
....				
....				
Snacks				
....				
....				
....				
TOTAL				

🌼 **NOTES**

Don't eat that, do eat this!

● BREAKFAST

Swap that... Blueberry muffin and full-fat milk latte to go. A small take-away coffee with a sugar-filled muffin can add up to over 500 calories (that's a quarter of the recommended daily 2,000 calorie intake for a woman).

For this... Porridge topped with sliced banana and chopped pecan nuts. The oats are rich in soluble fibre, which is a low-GI food and releases sugars slowly to keep you fuller for longer. Adding banana (or berries if you like!) is an easy way to get one of your recommended five-a-day fruits and vegetables. Nuts contain healthy fats that have been shown to help improve brain function and increase concentration if incorporated into your diet on a daily basis.

● LUNCH

Swap that... Classic sandwich of white bread, with turkey, bacon and mayo. White bread has almost no nutritional value, and many find that it makes them feel bloated (*so* not a good afternoon look). Plus, mayonnaise is packed with fats, as is bacon.

For this... Chunky vegetable soup with a wholemeal roll, followed by a yogurt and a piece of fresh fruit (see, when you pick the right foods, you can actually enjoy more!) Soup is any dieter's lunch of choice and it's light and filling, and wholemeal bread provides fibre (for healthy digestion). You can even afford to add a knob of butter to the roll since you're being so good! Yogurt provides calcium, which is essential for healthy bones, teeth, hair and nails – it's true: you are what you eat! Fresh fruit is a sweet treat that counts as another of those all important five-a-day.

● DINNER

Swap that... Chinese take-away. We've all been there, phoning for a take-away at the end of a long day... but an average serving of sweet and sour chicken with fried rice and prawn crackers can contain in excess of 1,500 calories. With that in mind, it's a no-brainer to make your own, more virtuous version.

For this... Chicken and vegetable stir-fry with brown rice. Chicken is a great all-rounder: filled with flavour, super-lean and high in protein – it's a must for dieters. Adding your favourite vegetables to any meal is a low-calorie way to increase volume and nutritional value. Brown rice should replace white rice in your storecupboard. Not only will it keep you fuller for longer, but it's packed with important B vitamins too.

Did you know?
A 100-ml/3½-fl oz measure of fruit juice counts as one of your five-a-day – but it has to be unsweetened juice.

Did you know?
Wholegrain foods (like granary bread, brown rice and wholewheat pasta) release sugars slowly, keeping you fuller for longer. Aim for 3–6 servings per day.

Did you know?
Peppermint tea is nature's tummy soother – it's a fantastic sickness remedy, ideal if you feel bloated or queasy after eating too much!

What did you eat today?

DATE

....

	Calories	Fat	Sat Fat	Carbs

● **Breakfast**

....

....

● **Lunch**

....

....

● **Dinner**

....

....

● **Snacks**

....

....

....

....

TOTAL

NOTES

What did you eat today?

	Calories	Fat	Sat Fat	Carbs

DATE
....

● **Breakfast**
....
....

● **Lunch**
....
....

● **Dinner**
....
....

● **Snacks**
....
....
....
....

TOTAL

NOTES

135

What did you eat today?

DATE

....

● **Breakfast**

....

....

● **Lunch**

....

....

● **Dinner**

....

....

● **Snacks**

....

....

....

....

	Calories	Fat	Sat Fat	Carbs
TOTAL				

✿ **NOTES**

What did you eat today?

DATE

	Calories	Fat	Sat Fat	Carbs

🔵 **Breakfast**

....

....

🔵 **Lunch**

....

....

🔵 **Dinner**

....

....

🔵 **Snacks**

....

....

....

....

TOTAL

✿ **NOTES**

What did you eat today?

DATE
....

	Calories	Fat	Sat Fat	Carbs

● **Breakfast**
....
....

● **Lunch**
....
....

● **Dinner**
....
....

● **Snacks**
....
....
....
....

TOTAL

⚙ **NOTES**

What did you eat today?

	Calories	Fat	Sat Fat	Carbs
DATE				

● **Breakfast**

● **Lunch**

● **Dinner**

● **Snacks**

	Calories	Fat	Sat Fat	Carbs
TOTAL				

✺ NOTES

CHOCOLATE
CHEAT

Low-cal coffee ice cream

● **SERVES 6**

55 g/2 oz dark chocolate
250 g/9 oz ricotta cheese
85 g/3 oz reduced-fat natural yogurt
70 g/2½ oz granulated sugar
175 ml/6 fl oz strong black coffee,
   cooled and chilled

½ tsp ground cinnamon
dash of vanilla extract

1. Grate the chocolate and set aside. Put the ricotta cheese, yogurt and sugar in a blender or food processor and process until a smooth purée forms. Transfer to a large bowl and beat in the coffee, cinnamon, vanilla extract and half of the grated chocolate.

2. Spoon the mixture into a freezerproof container and freeze for 1½ hours, or until slushy. Remove from the freezer, turn into a bowl and beat. Return to the container and freeze for 1½ hours.

3. Repeat this beating and freezing process two times before serving in scoops, decorated with the remaining grated chocolate. Alternatively, leave in the freezer until 15 minutes before serving, then transfer to the fridge to soften slightly before scooping.

● **TIP:** Homemade ice cream tends to harden over time if stored in the freezer for too long, but this ice cream will keep well for up to 3 months in a tightly sealed container.

Destiny is all about the choices we make and the chances we take!

This edition published by Exclusive Editions Publishing Ltd in 2013

Exclusive Editions Publishing Ltd
Chartist House
15–17 Trim Street
Bath BA1 1HA, UK
www.parragon.com

Project Managed by Alice Blackledge
Internal design by Amy Child

ISBN 978-1-4723-2980-6

Printed in China

NOTES FOR THE READER

This book uses both metric and imperial measurements. Follow the same units of measurement throughout; do not mix metric and imperial. All spoon measurements are level: teaspoons are assumed to be 5 ml, and tablespoons are assumed to be 15 ml. Unless otherwise stated, milk is assumed to be full fat, eggs and individual vegetables are medium, and pepper is freshly ground black pepper. Unless otherwise stated, all vegetables should be washed and peeled prior to using.

Garnishes, decorations and serving suggestions are all optional and not necessarily included in the recipe ingredients or method. Any optional ingredients and seasoning to taste are not included in the nutritional analysis. The times given are an approximate guide only. Preparation times differ according to the techniques used by different people and the cooking times may also vary from those given. Optional ingredients, variations or serving suggestions have not been included in the time calculations.

Consult your doctor before following any new diet or fitness plans.

PICTURE ACKNOWLEDGEMENTS

Page 62–63: Five food groups © Maximilian Stock Ltd/Getty Images